Julia Donaldson   Axel Scheffler

THE GRUFFALO
Activity Book

This book belongs to

....

MACMILLAN CHILDREN'S BOOKS

Step Inside the Deep Dark Wood

Draw in the missing characters
from the story and colour in the scene.

Let's get colouring!

The Gruffalo has terrible tusks and terrible claws,
and terrible teeth in his terrible jaws.
Can you complete the pictures?

Can you complete the pictures of the Gruffalo's knobbly knees, and turned-out toes, and the poisonous wart at the end of his nose?

complete this picture with purple prickles

He has purple prickles
all over his back.

Spot the Difference

Can you spot eight differences between the two scenes?

Circle the differences in the picture below.

Gruffalo Album

The Gruffalo is collecting pictures for his scrapbook and he needs your help.

Draw pictures to match the labels!

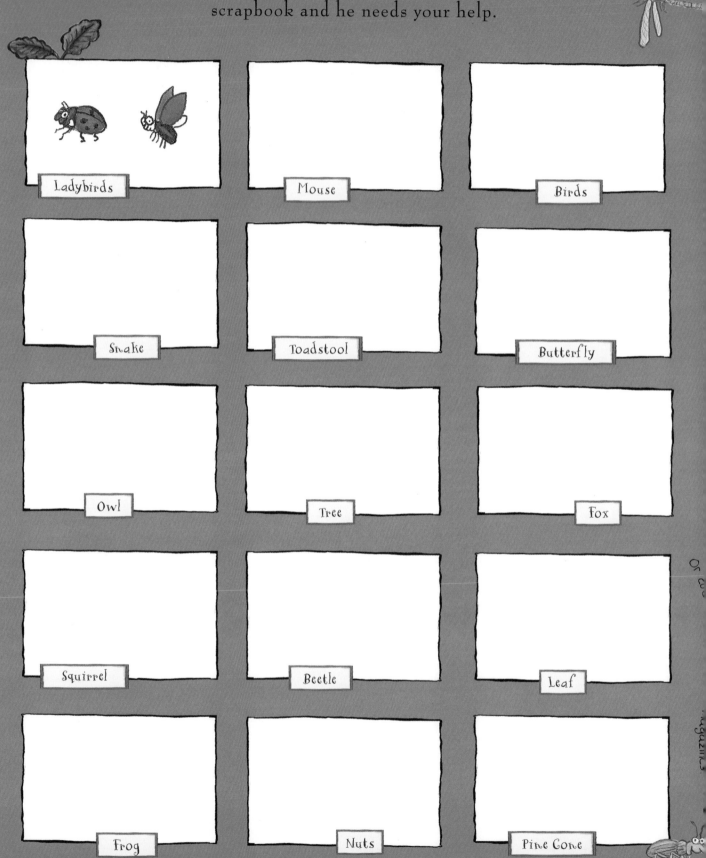

Ladybirds

Mouse

Birds

Snake

Toadstool

Butterfly

Owl

Tree

Fox

Squirrel

Beetle

Leaf

Frog

Nuts

Pine Cone

Mouse's Maze

Help Mouse find his way safely
through the deep dark wood.

Hooray! A happy mouse with a tasty nut.

Everyone's Different in the Deep Dark Wood!

Draw and colour in the pictures to complete the pairs of opposites.

big

small

we've done the first one for you

long

short

fast

slow

day   night

happy   sad

Animal Actions in the Deep Dark Wood

Who does what? Colour in the pictures, then write in
the animal names. We've done the first one for you!

flutter

like a b utterfly

squeak

like a m . . . .

scamper

like a f . . . . . .

flap

like a b . . . .

wriggle

like a s ....

jump

like a f ....

slither

like a s ....

hoot

like an o ......

and growl like the

G ....!

Where are You Going to, Little Brown Mouse?

Colour in this picture of Mouse and Snake.

Make a Monster

Draw your own monster!
What will your monster look like?

That's scary!

Where does your monster live?

What will you call him?

Come and Have Tea in My Treetop House

Colour in this picture of Mouse and Owl.

Colour in

Use your colouring pencils to fill in the snake's swirly pattern

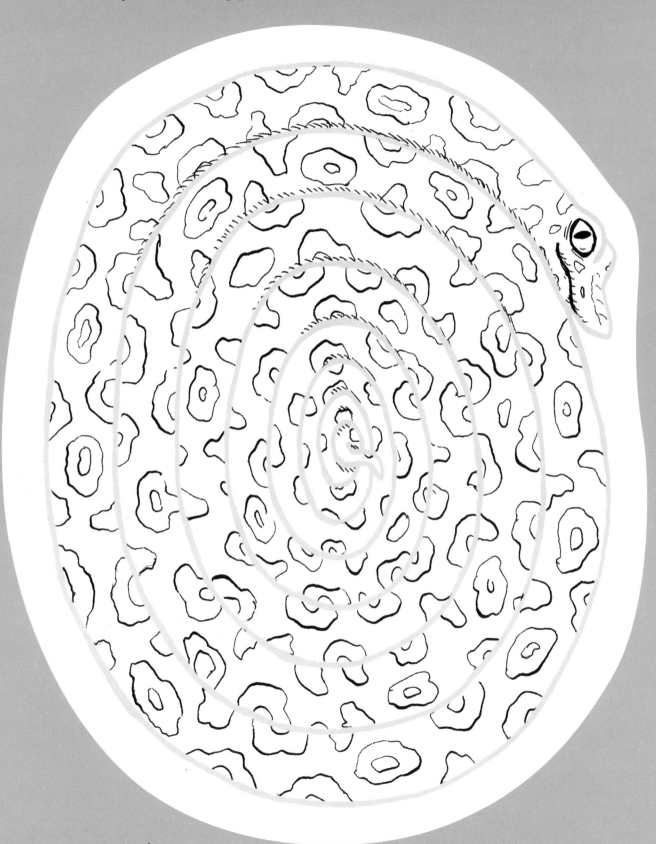

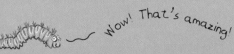 Wow! That's amazing!

Gruffalos Galore

Only two of these gruffalos are exactly the same.

Can you circle the matching pair?

Come and Have Lunch in My Underground House

Colour in the picture of Mouse and Fox.

Welcome to the deep dark wood! Do you know who all these characters are?

Colour them in . . . and why not add some more trees?

Shhh ... the Gruffalo is Asleep

What's he dreaming about?

Draw what you think it might be.

Zzzzzzzzzzzzzzzzzzzzzz!

Join the Dots

Complete this picture and colour it in!

Goodbye, Gruffalo!

Colour in the picture.